# JANE AUSTEN
## *A Treasury*

JANE AUSTEN: A TREASURY

Summersdale Publishers Ltd
46 West Street
Chichester
West Sussex
PO19 1RP
UK

www.summersdale.com

Printed and bound in the Czech Republic

ISBN: 978-1-84953-358-4

Substantial discounts on bulk quantities of Summersdale books are available to corporations, professional associations and other organisations. For details contact Nicky Douglas by telephone: +44 (0) 1243 756902, fax: +44 (0) 1243 786300 or email nicky@summersdale.com.

# Jane Austen

## *A Treasury*

Constance Moore

summersdale

# Contents

Pleasing

Conversation

*Mrs Allen was... never satisfied with the day unless she spent the chief of it by the side of Mrs Thorpe, in what they called conversation, but in which there was scarcely ever any exchange of opinion, and not often any resemblance of subject, for Mrs Thorpe talked chiefly of her children, and Mrs Allen of her gowns.*

*Northanger Abbey*

*She spoke with a confidence which staggered, with a satisfaction which silenced, Mr Knightley. She was in gay spirits, and would have prolonged the conversation, wanting to hear the particulars of his suspicions, every look described, and all the wheres and hows of a circumstance which highly entertained her: but his gaiety did not meet hers. He found he could not be useful, and his feelings were too much irritated for talking.*

*Emma, of Emma Woodhouse*

*'I certainly have not the talent which some people possess,' said Darcy, 'of conversing easily with those I have never seen before. I cannot catch their tone of conversation, or appear interested in their concerns, as I often see done.'*

*Pride and Prejudice*

*'My idea of good company... is the company of clever, well-informed people, who have a great deal of conversation; that is what I call good company.'*

*'You are mistaken,' said he gently, 'that is not good company, that is the best.'*

*Anne and Mr Elliot, Persuasion*

*She found, while they were at table, such a happy flow of conversation prevailing, in which she was not required to take any part – there was so much to be said between the brother and sister about Bath, so much between the two young men about hunting, so much of politics between Mr Crawford and Dr Grant, and of everything and all together between Mr Crawford and Mrs Grant, as to leave her the fairest prospect of having only to listen in quiet, and of passing a very agreeable day.*

*Mansfield Park,*
*of Fanny Price*

'My idea of him is, that he can adapt his conversation to the taste of every body, and has the power as well as the wish of being universally agreeable. To you, he will talk of farming; to me, of drawing or music; and so on to every body, having that general information on all subjects which will enable him to follow the lead, or take the lead, just as propriety may require, and to speak extremely well on each.'

*Emma Woodhouse on Mr Frank Churchill, Emma*

────────────◦○○◦────────────

*Their conversation turned upon those subjects, of which the free discussion has generally much to do in perfecting a sudden intimacy between two young ladies: such as dress, balls, flirtations, and quizzes.*

*Northanger Abbey*

I have *subdued him* entirely *by sentiment* and *serious* conversation, and made him, I may venture to say, at least *half in love* with me, *without the semblance* of the most commonplace *flirtation.*

*Lady Susan*

'Here is a young man wishing to pay his addresses to you, with everything to recommend him: not merely situation in life, fortune, and character, but with more than common agreeableness, with address and conversation pleasing to everybody.'

Sir Thomas Bertram on Mr Henry Crawford,
Mansfield Park

———————oOOo———————

*Marianne was silent; it was impossible for her to say what she did not feel, however trivial the occasion; and upon Elinor therefore the whole task of telling lies when politeness required it, always fell.*

Sense and Sensibility

———————oOOo———————

'Do you talk by rule, then, while you are dancing?'
'Sometimes. One must speak a little, you know. It would look odd to be entirely silent for half an hour together, and yet for the advantage of some, conversation ought to be so arranged as that they may have the trouble of saying as little as possible.'

Mr Darcy and Elizabeth Bennet, Pride and Prejudice

# Dress and Attire

*There she sat – and who would have guessed how many tears she had been lately shedding? To be in company, nicely dressed herself and seeing others nicely dressed, to sit and smile and look pretty, and say nothing, was enough for the happiness of the present hour.*

*Emma, of Emma Woodhouse*

*Dress was her passion. She had a most harmless delight in being fine; and our heroine's entrée into life could not take place till after three or four days had been spent in learning what was mostly worn, and her chaperone was provided with a dress of the newest fashion.*

*Northanger Abbey, of Mrs Allen*

*I bought some Japan ink likewise, and next week shall begin my operations on my hat, on which you know my principal hopes of happiness depend.*

*Letter to Cassandra*

———∞○○○∞———

*To her dress and appearance she was grown so perfectly indifferent, as not to bestow half the consideration on it, during the whole of her toilet, which it received from Miss Steele in the first five minutes of their being together, when it was finished.*

*Sense and Sensibility, of Marianne Dashwood*

*Her eldest daughter* had
great personal *beauty,* and the
younger ones, *by pretending*
*to be* as *handsome* as
their sister, imitating her air, and
*dressing* in the same style,
did *very* well.

*Northanger Abbey, of Mrs Thorpe*

*It would be mortifying to the feelings of many ladies, could they be made to understand how little the heart of man is affected by what is costly or new in their attire; how little it is biased by the texture of their muslin, and how unsusceptible of peculiar tenderness towards the spotted, the sprigged, the mull, or the jackonet.*

*Northanger Abbey*

*Mrs Elton then said, 'Nobody can think less of dress in general than I do – but upon such an occasion as this, when every body's eyes are so much upon me, and in compliment to the Westons – who I have no doubt are giving this ball chiefly to do me honour – I would not wish to be inferior to others. And I see very few pearls in the room except mine.'*

*Emma*

---

*'Lady Russell quite bores one with her new publications. You need not tell her so, but I thought her dress hideous the other night. I used to think she had some taste in dress, but I was ashamed of her at the concert. Something so formal and arrangé in her air! and she sits so upright!'*

*Elizabeth Elliot, Persuasion*

*I cannot help thinking that it is more natural to have flowers grow out of the head than fruit.*

*Letter to Cassandra, on hat trimmings*

---

'*There now, you are going to laugh at me too. But why should not I wear pink ribbons? I do not care if it is the Doctor's favourite colour. I am sure, for my part, I should never have known he did like it better than any other colour, if he had not happened to say so.*'

*Miss Steele, Sense and Sensibility*

---

'*Do you understand muslins, sir?*'

'*Particularly well; I always buy my own cravats, and am allowed to be an excellent judge; and my sister has often trusted me in the choice of a gown. I bought one for her the other day, and it was pronounced to be a prodigious bargain by every lady who saw it. I gave but five shillings a yard for it, and a true Indian muslin.*'

*Mrs Allen and Mr Tilney, Northanger Abbey*

# Dancing

'Did you not think, Mr Darcy, that I expressed myself uncommonly well just now, when I was teasing Colonel Forster to give us a ball at Meryton?'

'With great energy; but it is always a subject which makes a lady energetic.'

*Elizabeth Bennet and Mr Darcy, Pride and Prejudice*

---

'I should like balls infinitely better,' she replied, 'if they were carried on in a different manner; but there is something insufferably tedious in the usual process of such a meeting. It would surely be much more rational if conversation instead of dancing were made the order of the day.'

'Much more rational, my dear Caroline, I dare say, but it would not be near so much like a ball.'

*Caroline and Charles Bingley, Pride and Prejudice*

It was a *splendid sight,* and she began, *for the first time that evening,* to feel herself at a ball: she longed to *dance,* but she had *not an acquaintance* in the room.

*Northanger Abbey, of Catherine Morland*

*'Here have I been telling all my acquaintances that I was going to dance with the prettiest girl in the room; and when they see you standing up with somebody else, they will quiz me famously.'*

John Thorpe, Northanger Abbey

*The melancholy part was, to see so many dozen young women standing by without partners, and each of them with two ugly naked shoulders.*

Letter to Cassandra

*'Open the windows! – but surely, Mr Churchill, nobody would think of opening the windows at Randalls. Nobody could be so imprudent! I never heard of such a thing. Dancing with open windows!'*

Mr Woodhouse, Emma

*It may be possible to do without dancing entirely. Instances have been known of young people passing many, many months successively, without being at any ball of any description, and no material injury accrue either to body or mind; – but when a beginning is made – when the felicities of rapid motion have once been, though slightly, felt – it must be a very heavy set that does not ask for more.*

*Emma*

'A dance!' cried Marianne. 'Impossible! Who is to dance?'

'Who! why yourselves, and the Careys, and Whitakers to be sure – What! you thought nobody could dance because a certain person that shall be nameless is gone!'

*Marianne Dashwood and Mrs Jennings,*
*Sense and Sensibility*

<hr />

'What a charming amusement for young people this is, Mr Darcy! There is nothing like dancing after all. I consider it as one of the first refinements of polished society.'

'Certainly, sir; and it has the advantage also of being in vogue amongst the less polished societies of the world. Every savage can dance.'

*Sir William Lucas and Mr Darcy, Pride and Prejudice*

*This was an affair, however, of which Lady Middleton did not approve. In the country, an unpremeditated dance was very allowable; but in London, where the reputation of elegance was more important and less easily attained, it was risking too much for the gratification of a few girls, to have it known that Lady Middleton had given a small dance of eight or nine couple, with two violins, and a mere side-board collation.*

*Sense and Sensibility*

―――――∞○○○∞―――――

*Nothing could be more delightful! To be fond of dancing was a certain step towards falling in love.*

*Pride and Prejudice*

Music

*The evening ended with dancing. On its being proposed, Anne offered her services, as usual; and though her eyes would sometimes fill with tears as she sat at the instrument, she was extremely glad to be employed, and desired nothing in return but to be unobserved.*

*Persuasion*

*His pleasure in music, though it amounted not to that ecstatic delight which alone could sympathize with her own, was estimable when contrasted against the horrible insensibility of the others; and she was reasonable enough to allow that a man of five and thirty might well have outlived all acuteness of feeling and every exquisite power of enjoyment. She was perfectly disposed to make every allowance for the colonel's advanced state of life which humanity required.*

*Sense and Sensibility, of Marianne Dashwood's opinion of Colonel Brandon*

'I remember one proof of her being thought to play well: – a man, a very musical man, and in love with another woman – engaged to her – on the point of marriage – would yet never ask that other woman to sit down to the instrument, if the lady in question could sit down instead – never seemed to like to hear one if he could hear the other. That, I thought, in a man of known musical talent, was some proof.'

Mr Frank Churchill on Jane Fairfax, Emma

———

The party, like other musical parties, comprehended a great many people who had real taste for the performance, and a great many more who had none at all; and the performers themselves were, as usual, in their own estimation, and that of their immediate friends, the first private performers in England.

Sense and Sensibility

'There is a *fine old saying*, which everybody here is of course *familiar with*: "Keep your breath to cool your *porridge*"; and I shall keep mine to swell *my song*.'

Elizabeth Bennet, *Pride and Prejudice*

'Of music! Then pray speak aloud. It is of all subjects my delight. I must have my share in the conversation if you are speaking of music. There are few people in England, I suppose, who have more true enjoyment of music than myself, or a better natural taste. If I had ever learnt, I should have been a great proficient.'

Lady Catherine de Burgh,
Pride and Prejudice

'But,' said I, 'to be quite honest, I do not think I can live without something of a musical society. I condition for nothing else, but without music, life would be a blank to me.'

*Emma Woodhouse, Emma*

---

Edmund spoke of the harp as his favourite instrument, and hoped to be soon allowed to hear her. Fanny had never heard the harp at all, and wished for it very much.

'I shall be most happy to play to you both,' said Miss Crawford; 'at least as long as you can like to listen: probably much longer, for I dearly love music myself, and where the natural taste is equal the player must always be best off, for she is gratified in more ways than one.'

*Mansfield Park*

*Lady Middleton frequently called him to order, wondered how any one's attention could be diverted from music for a moment, and asked Marianne to sing a particular song which Marianne had just finished.*

*Sense and Sensibility*

---

*'The little Durands were there, I conclude,' said she, 'with their mouths open to catch the music, like unfledged sparrows ready to be fed. They never miss a concert.'*

*Mrs Smith, Persuasion*

Literature

*'Oh! It is only a novel!' replies the young lady, while she lays down her book with affected indifference, or momentary shame. 'It is only Cecilia, or Camilla, or Belinda'; or, in short, only some work in which the greatest powers of the mind are displayed, in which the most thorough knowledge of human nature, the happiest delineation of its varieties, the liveliest effusions of wit and humour, are conveyed to the world in the best-chosen language.*

*Northanger Abbey*

—————————:o0O0o:—————————

*Because they were fond of reading, she fancied them satirical: perhaps without exactly knowing what it was to be satirical; but that did not signify.*

*Sense and Sensibility, of Lady Middleton's opinion of Elinor and Marianne Dashwood*

'I think you must like Udolpho, if you were to read it; it is so very interesting.'

'Not I, faith! No, if I read anything, it shall be Mrs Radcliffe's; her novels are amusing enough; they are worth reading; some fun and nature in them.'

'Udolpho was written by Mrs Radcliffe,' said Catherine, with some hesitation, from the fear of mortifying him.

Catherine Morland and John Thorpe,
Northanger Abbey

———◦◦◯◦◦———

The truth was that Sir Edward, whom circumstances had confined very much to one spot, had read more sentimental novels than agreed with him.

Sanditon

———◦◦◯◦◦———

'The person, be it gentleman or lady, who has not pleasure in a good novel, must be intolerably stupid.'

Henry Tilney, Northanger Abbey

'I do not think I ever opened a book in my life which had not something to say upon woman's inconstancy. Songs and proverbs, all talk of woman's fickleness. But perhaps, you will say, these were all written by men.'

'Perhaps I shall. Yes, yes, if you please, no reference to examples in books. Men have had every advantage of us in telling their own story. Education has been theirs in so much higher a degree; the pen has been in their hands. I will not allow books to prove anything.'

Captain Harville and Anne Elliot, Persuasion

*I could not sit seriously down to write a serious romance under any other motive than to save my life, and if it were indispensable for me to keep it up and never relax into laughing at myself or other people, I am sure I should be hung before I had finished the first chapter.*

Letter to James Stanier Clarke

———————oOOOoo———————

*The subject of reading aloud was farther discussed. The two young men were the only talkers, but they, standing by the fire, talked over the too common neglect of the qualification, the total inattention to it, in the ordinary school-system for boys, the consequently natural, yet in some instances almost unnatural, degree of ignorance and uncouthness of men, of sensible and well-informed men, when suddenly called to the necessity of reading aloud, which had fallen within their notice, giving instances of blunders, and failures with their secondary causes, the want of management of the voice, of proper modulation and emphasis, of foresight and judgment, all proceeding from the first cause: want of early attention and habit.*

Mansfield Park

Provided that nothing like *useful knowledge* could be gained from them, provided they were all story and *no reflection*, she had never any objection to books *at all*.

*Northanger Abbey, of Catherine Morland*

*'And books! – Thomson, Cowper, Scott – she would buy them all over and over again: she would buy up every copy, I believe, to prevent their falling into unworthy hands; and she would have every book that tells her how to admire an old twisted tree. Should not you, Marianne?'*

Edward Ferrars, Sense and Sensibility

---

*'What think you of books?' said he, smiling.*

*'Books – oh! no. I am sure we never read the same, or not with the same feelings.'*

*'I am sorry you think so; but if that be the case, there can at least be no want of subject. We may compare our different opinions.'*

*'No – I cannot talk of books in a ball-room; my head is always full of something else.'*

*'The present always occupies you in such scenes – does it?' said he, with a look of doubt.*

Mr Darcy and Elizabeth Bennet, Pride and Prejudice

# Accomplishments

*She was not much deceived as to her own skill either as an artist or a musician, but she was not unwilling to have others deceived, or sorry to know her reputation for accomplishment often higher than it deserved.*

*Emma, of Emma Woodhouse*

———————⚬O○○○⚬—————————

*There was a numerous family; but the only two grown up, excepting Charles, were Henrietta and Louisa, young ladies of nineteen and twenty, who had brought from school at Exeter all the usual stock of accomplishments, and were now like thousands of other young ladies, living to be fashionable, happy, and merry.*

*Persuasion*

'And besides all this, I am afraid, Mama, he has no real taste. Music seems scarcely to attract him, and though he admires Elinor's drawings very much, it is not the admiration of a person who can understand their worth. It is evident, in spite of his frequent attention to her while she draws, that in fact he knows nothing of the matter.'

*Marianne Dashwood on Edward Ferrars,*
*Sense and Sensibility*

Mrs Goddard was the mistress of a School – not of a seminary, or an establishment, or any thing which professed, in long sentences of refined nonsense, to combine liberal acquirements with elegant morality, upon new principles and new systems – and where young ladies for enormous pay might be screwed out of health and into vanity – but a real, honest, old-fashioned Boarding-school, where a reasonable quantity of accomplishments were sold at a reasonable price, and where girls might be sent to be out of the way, and scramble themselves into a little education, without any danger of coming back prodigies.

*Emma*

'A woman must have a thorough knowledge of music, singing, drawing, dancing, and the modern languages, to deserve the word; and besides all this, she must possess a certain something in her air and manner of walking, the tone of her voice, her address and expressions, or the word will be but half-deserved.'

'All this she must possess,' added Darcy, 'and to all this she must yet add something more substantial, in the improvement of her mind by extensive reading.'

*Miss Bingley and Mr Darcy,*
*Pride and Prejudice*

'That is *what I like;* that is what a **young man** ought to be. Whatever be his pursuits, *his eagerness* in them should know *no moderation,* and *leave him* no sense of fatigue.'

*Marianne Dashwood, Sense and Sensibility*

'I have not had the pleasure of visiting in Camden Place so long,' replied he, 'without knowing something of Miss Anne Elliot; and I do regard her as one who is too modest for the world in general to be aware of half her accomplishments, and too highly accomplished for modesty to be natural in any other woman.'

*Mr Elliot, Persuasion*

―――――∞○○○∞―――――

So far her improvement was sufficient – and in many other points she came on exceedingly well; for though she could not write sonnets, she brought herself to read them; and though there seemed no chance of her throwing a whole party into raptures by a prelude on the pianoforte, of her own composition, she could listen to other people's performance with very little fatigue.

*Northanger Abbey, of Catherine Morland*

# Manners

# and Faults

*Lydia was occasionally a visitor there, when her husband was gone to enjoy himself in London or Bath; and with the Bingleys they both of them frequently staid so long, that even Bingley's good humour was overcome, and he proceeded so far as to talk of giving them a hint to be gone.*

*Pride and Prejudice*

———○○○○○———

*'Oh! dear, how beautiful these are! Well! how delightful! Do but look, mama, how sweet! I declare they are quite charming; I could look at them for ever.' And then sitting down again, she very soon forgot that there were any such things in the room.*

*Mrs Palmer on drawings, Sense and Sensibility*

'Mr Wickham is blessed with such happy manners as may ensure his making friends – whether he may be equally capable of retaining them, is less certain.'

Mr Darcy, Pride and Prejudice

*I do not want people to be very agreeable, as it saves me the trouble of liking them a great deal.*

*Letter to Cassandra*

———oOOOo———

*Mr Knightley, in fact, was one of the few people who could see faults in Emma Woodhouse, and the only one who ever told her of them: and though this was not particularly agreeable to Emma herself, she knew it would be so much less so to her father, that she would not have him really suspect such a circumstance as her not being thought perfect by every body.*

*Emma*

———oOOOo———

*She was a benevolent, charitable, good woman, and capable of strong attachments, most correct in her conduct, strict in her notions of decorum, and with manners that were held a standard of good-breeding. She had a cultivated mind, and was, generally speaking, rational and consistent; but she had prejudices on the side of ancestry; she had a value for rank and consequence, which blinded her a little to the faults of those who possessed them.*

*Persuasion, of Lady Russell*

'I am sure she will make a very good servant: she is a civil, pretty-spoken girl; I have a great opinion of her. Whenever I see her, she always curtseys and asks me how I do, in a very pretty manner; and when you have had her here to do needlework, I observe she always turns the lock of the door the right way and never bangs it.'

Mr Woodhouse, *Emma*

'The power of doing anything with quickness is always prized much by the possessor, and often without any attention to the imperfection of the performance. When you told Mrs Bennet this morning that if you ever resolved upon quitting Netherfield you should be gone in five minutes, you meant it to be a sort of panegyric, of compliment to yourself – and yet what is there so very laudable in a precipitance which must leave very necessary business undone, and can be of no real advantage to yourself or anyone else?'

*Mr Darcy to Mr Bingley, Pride and Prejudice*

'He is just what a young man ought to be,' said she, 'sensible, good-humoured, lively; and I never saw such happy manners! – so much ease, with such perfect good breeding!'

'He is also handsome,' replied Elizabeth, 'which a young man ought likewise to be, if he possibly can. His character is thereby complete.'

*Jane and Elizabeth Bennet on Mr Bingley, Pride and Prejudice*

*He was not an ill-disposed young man, unless to be rather cold hearted and rather selfish is to be ill-disposed: but he was, in general, well respected; for he conducted himself with propriety in the discharge of his ordinary duties.*

Sense and Sensibility, of Mr John Dashwood

---

*He was a stout young man of middling height, who, with a plain face and ungraceful form, seemed fearful of being too handsome unless he wore the dress of a groom, and too much like a gentleman unless he were easy where he ought to be civil, and impudent where he might be allowed to be easy.*

Northanger Abbey, of John Thorpe

# Men and
# Women

'For it is many months since I have considered her as one of the handsomest women of my acquaintance.'

*Mr Darcy on Elizabeth Bennet, Pride and Prejudice*

---

The Miss Dashwoods were young, pretty, and unaffected. It was enough to secure his good opinion; for to be unaffected was all that a pretty girl could want to make her mind as captivating as her person.

*Sense and Sensibility*

*But when a young lady is to be a heroine, the perverseness of forty surrounding families cannot prevent her. Something must and will happen to throw a hero in her way.*

Northanger Abbey

'Warmth and tenderness of heart, with an affectionate, open manner, will beat all the cleverness of head in the world, for attraction: I am sure it will.'

Emma Woodhouse, *Emma*

————————⊃□○○○□⊂————————

There are certainly not so many men of large fortune in the world, as there are pretty women to deserve them.

*Mansfield Park*

'Man is more robust than woman, but he is not longer lived; which exactly explains my view of the nature of their attachments.'

*Anne Elliot, Persuasion*

---

'I think very highly of the understanding of all the women in the world – especially of those – whoever they may be – with whom I happen to be in company.'

*Henry Tilney, Northanger Abbey*

---

Elinor placed all that was astonishing in this way of acting to his mother's account; and it was happy for her that he had a mother whose character was so imperfectly known to her, as to be the general excuse for every thing strange on the part of her son.

*Sense and Sensibility*

'That would be the greatest misfortune of all! – to find a man agreeable whom one is determined to hate!'

Elizabeth Bennet, *Pride and Prejudice*

'I never in my life saw a man more intent on being agreeable than Mr Elton. It is downright labour to him where ladies are concerned. With men he can be rational and unaffected, but when he has ladies to please, every feature works.'

*John Knightley, Emma*

'But I hate to hear you talking so like a fine gentleman, and as if women were all fine ladies, instead of rational creatures. We none of us expect to be in smooth water all our days.'

*Captain Frederick Wentworth's sister, Persuasion*

# Class and Fortune

'What have wealth or grandeur to do with happiness?'

'Grandeur has but little,' said Elinor, 'but wealth has much to do with it.'

*Marianne and Elinor Dashwood, Sense and Sensibility*

———•oOOo•———

Mary was in a state of mind to rejoice in a connexion with the Bertram family, and to be not displeased with her brother's marrying a little beneath him.

*Mansfield Park*

*'If they had uncles enough to fill all Cheapside,'*
*cried Bingley, 'it would not make them one jot less*
*agreeable.'*
*'But it must very materially lessen their chance of*
*marrying men of any consideration in the world,'*
*replied Darcy.*

*Pride and Prejudice*

*Harriet's parentage became known. She proved*
*to be the daughter of a tradesman, rich enough to*
*afford her the comfortable maintenance which had*
*ever been hers, and decent enough to have always*
*wished for concealment – Such was the blood of*
*gentility which Emma had formerly been so ready*
*to vouch for! – It was likely to be as untainted,*
*perhaps, as the blood of many a gentleman: but*
*what a connexion had she been preparing for Mr*
*Knightley – or for the Churchills – or even for Mr*
*Elton! – The stain of illegitimacy, unbleached by*
*nobility or wealth, would have been a stain indeed.*

*Emma*

*The whole of Lucy's behaviour in the affair, and the prosperity which crowned it, therefore, may be held forth as a most encouraging instance of what an earnest, an unceasing attention to self-interest, however its progress may be apparently obstructed, will do in securing every advantage of fortune, with no other sacrifice than that of time and conscience.*

*Sense and Sensibility*

'The world is blinded by his fortune and consequence, or frightened by his high and imposing manners, and sees him only as he chooses to be seen.'

*Mr Wickham on Mr Darcy, Pride and Prejudice*

***

'A young farmer, whether on horseback or on foot, is the very last sort of person to raise my curiosity. The yeomanry are precisely the order of people with whom I feel I can have nothing to do. A degree or two lower, and a creditable appearance might interest me; I might hope to be useful to their families in some way or other. But a farmer can need none of my help, and is, therefore, in one sense, as much above my notice as in every other he is below it.'

*Emma Woodhouse, Emma*

'The *interest* of *two thousand pounds* – how can a man *live on* it? – and when to that is added the recollection, that he might, but for his *own folly*, within three months have been in the receipt of two thousand, five hundred a-year (for Miss Morton has thirty thousand pounds,) I cannot picture to myself a more *wretched condition.*'

*Mr John Dashwood, Sense and Sensibility*

'... *were she prosperous, I could allow much for the occasional prevalence of the ridiculous over the good. Were she a woman of fortune, I would leave every harmless absurdity to take its chance, I would not quarrel with you for any liberties of manner. Were she your equal in situation – but, Emma, consider how far this is from being the case. She is poor; she has sunk from the comforts she was born to; and, if she live to old age, must probably sink more. Her situation should secure your compassion.'*

Mr Knightley on Miss Bates, Emma

---

*The dinner was a grand one, the servants were numerous, and every thing bespoke the Mistress's inclination for show, and the Master's ability to support it.*

Sense and Sensibility

---

*But Mrs Morland knew so little of lords and baronets, that she entertained no notion of their general mischievousness, and was wholly unsuspicious of danger to her daughter from their machinations.*

Northanger Abbey

# Gossip and Insults

Mr Richard Harvey is going to be *married*; but as it is a *great secret* and only *known* to half the *neighbourhood*, you must not *mention it.*

*Letter to Cassandra*

*... no poverty of any kind, except of conversation, appeared – but there, the deficiency was considerable. John Dashwood had not much to say for himself that was worth hearing, and his wife had still less.*

*Sense and Sensibility*

━━━━━━━━━○○○○━━━━━━━━

*Mrs Portman is not much admired in Dorsetshire; the good-natured world as usual extolled her beauty so highly that all the neighbourhood have had the pleasure of being disappointed.*

*Letter to Cassandra*

━━━━━━━━━○○○○━━━━━━━━

*There certainly were a dreadful multitude of ugly women in Bath; and as for the men! they were infinitely worse.*

*Persuasion*

*Mrs Allen was one of that numerous class of females, whose society can raise no other emotion than surprise at there being any men in the world who could like them well enough to marry them. She had neither beauty, genius, accomplishment, nor manner.*

*Northanger Abbey*

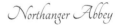

'A clergyman has nothing to do but be slovenly and selfish; read the newspaper, watch the weather, and quarrel with his wife. His curate does all the work and the business of his own life is to dine.'

*Miss Crawford, Mansfield Park*

'Brandon is just the kind of man,' said Willoughby one day, when they were talking of him together, 'whom every body speaks well of, and nobody cares about; whom all are delighted to see, and nobody remembers to talk to.'

*Sense and Sensibility*

*Another stupid party last night; perhaps if larger they might be less intolerable, but here there were only just enough to make one card-table, with six people to look on and talk nonsense to each other.*

*Letter to Cassandra*

* * *

*Lady Middleton was more agreeable than her mother only in being more silent.*

*Sense and Sensibility*

*The Miss Maitlands are both prettyish... with brown skins, large dark eyes, and a good deal of nose. – The General has got the gout, and Mrs Maitland the jaundice. – Miss Debary, Susan and Sally... made their appearance, and I was as civil to them as their bad breath would allow me.*

*Letter to Cassandra*

'She is a shrewd, intelligent, sensible woman. Hers is a line for seeing human nature; and she has a fund of good sense and observation, which, as a companion, make her infinitely superior to thousands of those who having only received "the best education in the world," know nothing worth attending to. Call it gossip, if you will, but when Nurse Rooke has half an hour's leisure to bestow on me, she is sure to have something to relate that is entertaining and profitable: something that makes one know one's species better. One likes to hear what is going on, to be au fait as to the newest modes of being trifling and silly. To me, who live so much alone, her conversation, I assure you, is a treat.'

*Mrs Smith, Persuasion*

'For what do we live,
but to make sport for
our neighbours, and
laugh at them
in our turn?'

Mr Bennet, Pride and Prejudice

# Men in Uniform

*There was one gentleman, an officer of the Cheshire, a very good-looking young man, who, I was told, wanted very much to be introduced to me, but as he did not want it quite enough to take much trouble in effecting it, we never could bring it about.*

*Letter to Cassandra*

―――――――□○○○○□―――――――

*'She was convinced of sailors having more worth and warmth than any other set of men in England; that they only knew how to live, and they only deserved to be respected and loved.'*

*Louisa Musgrove, Persuasion*

*Denny addressed them directly, and entreated permission to introduce his friend, Mr Wickham, who had returned with him the day before from town, and he was happy to say had accepted a commission in their corps. This was exactly as it should be; for the young man wanted only regimentals to make him completely charming.*

*Pride and Prejudice*

———∞○○○∞———

'We are not all born to be handsome. The sea is no beautifier, certainly; sailors do grow old betimes; I have observed it; they soon lose the look of youth. But then, is not it the same with many other professions, perhaps most other? Soldiers, in active service, are not at all better off: and even in the quieter professions, there is a toil and a labour of the mind, if not of the body, which seldom leaves a man's looks to the natural effect of time.'

*Mrs Clay, Persuasion*

'I remember the time when I liked a red coat myself very well – and, indeed, so I do still at my heart; and if a smart young colonel, with five or six thousand a year, should want one of my girls I shall not say nay to him.'

Mrs Bennet, Pride and Prejudice

*It was evident how little the women were used to the sight of anything tolerable, by the effect which a man of decent appearance produced. He had never walked anywhere arm-in-arm with Colonel Wallis (who was a fine military figure, though sandy-haired) without observing that every woman's eye was upon him; every woman's eye was sure to be upon Colonel Wallis.*

*Persuasion*

━━━━━━━━━━:ooＯoo:━━━━━━━━━━

*They could talk of nothing but officers; and Mr Bingley's large fortune, the mention of which gave animation to their mother, was worthless in their eyes when opposed to the regimentals of an ensign.*

*Pride and Prejudice, of Kitty and Lydia Bennet*

'Nothing but love, flirtation, and officers have been in her head.'

*Elizabeth Bennet, Pride and Prejudice*

*'I quite agree with my father in thinking a sailor might be a very desirable tenant. I have known a good deal of the profession; and besides their liberality, they are so neat and careful in all their ways!'*

*Mrs Clay, Persuasion*

---

*The first week of their return was soon gone. The second began. It was the last of the regiment's stay in Meryton, and all the young ladies in the neighbourhood were drooping apace. The dejection was almost universal. The elder Miss Bennets alone were still able to eat, drink, and sleep, and pursue the usual course of their employments. Very frequently were they reproached for this insensibility by Kitty and Lydia, whose own misery was extreme, and who could not comprehend such hardheartedness in any of the family.*

*Pride and Prejudice*

# Health and

# Exercise

*Elizabeth continued her walk alone, crossing field after field at a quick pace, jumping over stiles and springing over puddles with impatient activity, and finding herself at last within view of the house, with weary ankles, dirty stockings, and a face glowing with the warmth of exercise.*

*Pride and Prejudice*

———————oOOo———————

'*I am very sorry to hear, Miss Fairfax, of your being out this morning in the rain. Young ladies should take care of themselves. – Young ladies are delicate plants. They should take care of their health and their complexion.*'

*Mr Woodhouse, Emma*

*Within doors there was Lady Catherine, books, and a billiard-table, but gentlemen cannot always be within doors; and in the nearness of the Parsonage, or the pleasantness of the walk to it, or of the people who lived in it, the two cousins found a temptation from this period of walking thither almost every day.*

*Pride and Prejudice*

———∞○○○∞———

*One fatal swoon has cost me my Life... Beware of swoons, Dear Laura... A frenzy fit is not one quarter so pernicious; it is an exercise to the body and if not too violent, is, I dare say, conducive to health in its consequences – run mad as often as you chuse; but do not faint.*

*Love and Freindship*

'You take delight in vexing me. You have no compassion for my poor nerves.'

'You mistake me, my dear. I have a high respect for your nerves. They are my old friends. I have heard you mention them with consideration these last twenty years at least.'

Mrs and Mr Bennet,
Pride and Prejudice

*Had she found Jane in any apparent danger, Mrs Bennet would have been very miserable; but being satisfied on seeing her that her illness was not alarming, she had no wish of her recovering immediately, as her restoration to health would probably remove her from Netherfield.*

*Pride and Prejudice*

———∞○○○∞———

*'But now you love a hyacinth. So much the better. You have gained a new source of enjoyment, and it is well to have as many holds upon happiness as possible. Besides, a taste for flowers is always desirable in your sex, as a means of getting you out of doors, and tempting you to more frequent exercise than you would otherwise take.'*

*Henry Tilney, Northanger Abbey*

'Miss Eliza Bennet, let me persuade you to follow my example, and take a turn about the room. I assure you it is very refreshing after sitting so long in one attitude.'

*Miss Bingley, Pride and Prejudice*

---

'Don't keep coughing so, Kitty, for Heaven's sake! Have a little compassion on my nerves. You tear them to pieces.'

'Kitty has no discretion in her coughs,' said her father; 'she times them ill.'

'I do not cough for my own amusement,' replied Kitty fretfully.

*Pride and Prejudice*

---

I continue quite well; in proof of which I have bathed again this morning. It was absolutely necessary that I should have the little fever and indisposition which I had: it has been all the fashion this week in Lyme.

*Letter to Cassandra*

'You are *conscious* that your *figures appear* to the *greatest* advantage in walking... I can *admire* you much *better* as I sit *by the fire.*'

Mr Darcy, Pride and Prejudice

*Love*

'I never saw a more promising inclination; he was growing quite inattentive to other people, and wholly engrossed by her. Every time they met, it was more decided and remarkable. At his own ball he offended two or three young ladies, by not asking them to dance; and I spoke to him twice myself, without receiving an answer. Could there be finer symptoms? Is not general incivility the very essence of love?'

*Elizabeth Bennet on Mr Bingley, Pride and Prejudice*

―――――∞○○○∞―――――

When he was present she had no eyes for anyone else. Everything he did was right. Everything he said was clever. If their evenings at the Park were concluded with cards, he cheated himself and all the rest of the party to get her a good hand. If dancing formed the amusement of the night, they were partners for half the time; and when obliged to separate for a couple of dances, were careful to stand together, and scarcely spoke a word to anybody else. Such conduct made them, of course, most exceedingly laughed at; but ridicule could not shame, and seemed hardly to provoke them.

*Sense and Sensibility, of John Willoughby and Marianne Dashwood*

*Without supposing them, from what she saw, to be very seriously in love, their preference of each other was plain enough to make her a little uneasy.*

*Pride and Prejudice, of Mrs Gardiner*

———○○○○○———

'*I can listen no longer in silence. I must speak to you by such means as are within my reach. You pierce my soul. I am half agony, half hope. Tell me not that I am too late, that such precious feelings are gone for ever. I offer myself to you again with a heart even more your own than when you almost broke it, eight years and a half ago. Dare not say that man forgets sooner than woman, that his love has an earlier death. I have loved none but you. Unjust I may have been, weak and resentful I have been, but never inconstant.*'

*Captain Frederick Wentworth to Anne Elliott, Persuasion*

'I do, I do like him, I love him. Indeed he has no improper pride. He is perfectly amiable. You do not know what he really is; then pray do not pain me by speaking of him in such terms.'

*Elizabeth Bennet on Mr Darcy, Pride and Prejudice*

---

'I passed the happiest moments of my Life; Our time was most delightfully spent, in mutual Protestations of Freindship, and in vows of unalterable Love, in which we were secure from being interrupted, by intruding and disagreeable Visitors.'

*Laura, Love and Freindship*

*The happiness was such as he had probably never felt before; and he expressed himself on the occasion as sensibly and as warmly as a man violently in love can be supposed to do.*

Pride and Prejudice, of Mr Darcy

*His happiness in knowing himself to have been so long the beloved of such a heart, must have been great enough to warrant any strength of language in which he could clothe it to her or to himself; it must have been a delightful happiness.*

*Mansfield Park, of Edmund Bertram*

---

*That is the only kind of love I would give a farthing for – There is some sense in being in love at first sight.*

*Love and Freindship*

'I assure you it was a great compliment if he was, for he hardly ever falls in love with any body.'

Mrs Palmer on Colonel Brandon, Sense and Sensibility

'I suppose there may be a hundred different ways of being in love.'

*Emma Woodhouse, Emma*

─────────────00O0oc─────────────

'You must allow me to tell you how ardently I admire and love you.'

*Mr Darcy, Pride and Prejudice*

─────────────00O0oc─────────────

Do not be in a hurry, the right man will come at last; you will in the course of the next two or three years meet with somebody more generally unexceptionable than anyone you have yet known, who will love you as warmly as possible, and who will so completely attach you that you will feel you never really loved before.

*Letter to Fanny Knight*

# Courtship

'I lay it down as a general rule, Harriet, that if a woman doubts as to whether she should accept a man or not, she certainly ought to refuse him. If she can hesitate as to "Yes", she ought to say "No" directly. It is not a state to be safely entered into with doubtful feelings, with half a heart.'

*Emma Woodhouse, Emma*

'You really have done your hair in a more heavenly style than ever; you mischievous creature, do you want to attract everybody? I assure you, my brother is quite in love with you already.'

*Isabella Thorpe, Northanger Abbey*

It requires *uncommon steadiness of reason* to resist the *attraction* of being called *the most charming girl in the world.*

*Northanger Abbey*

*Half the sum of attraction, on either side, might have been enough, for he had nothing to do, and she had hardly anybody to love; but the encounter of such lavish recommendations could not fail. They were gradually acquainted, and when acquainted, rapidly and deeply in love.*

*Persuasion, of Captain Frederick Wentworth and Anne Elliot*

*No young lady can be justified in falling in love before the gentleman's love is declared, it must be very improper that a young lady should dream of a gentleman before the gentleman is first known to have dreamt of her.*

*Northanger Abbey*

'I would advise you by all means not to give him any encouragement. He generally pays attention to every new girl; but he is a great flirt, and never means anything serious.'

Miss Watson on Tom Musgrave, *The Watsons*

⸻◦◦○○◦◦⸻

The idea soon reached to conviction, as she observed his increasing civilities toward herself, and heard his frequent attempt at a compliment on her wit and vivacity; and though more astonished than gratified herself by this effect of her charms, it was not long before her mother gave her to understand that the probability of their marriage was extremely agreeable to her.

*Pride and Prejudice,* of Mr Collins' advances to Elizabeth Bennet

*Mr Rushworth… being inclined to marry, soon fancied himself in love. He was a heavy young man, with not more than common sense; but as there was nothing disagreeable in his figure or address, the young lady was well pleased with her conquest.*

Mansfield Park

'Well, it don't signify talking; but when a young man, be who he will, comes and makes love to a pretty girl, and promises marriage, he has no business to fly off from his word only because he grows poor, and a richer girl is ready to have him.'

*Mrs Jennings, Sense and Sensibility*

Yes, quite a proposal of marriage; and a very good letter, at least she thought so. And he wrote as if he really loved her very much – but she did not know.

*Emma, of Mr Martin's proposal to Harriet Smith*

# Rubs and

# Disappointments

'Nay, Mama, if he is not to be animated by Cowper! – but we must allow for difference of taste. Elinor has not my feelings, and therefore she may overlook it, and be happy with him. But it would have broke MY heart, had I loved him, to hear him read with so little sensibility.'

*Marianne Dashwood on Edward Ferrars,*
*Sense and Sensibility*

———∞OᴏOᴏ∞———

'There will be little rubs and disappointments everywhere, and we are all apt to expect too much; but then, if one scheme of happiness fails, human nature turns to another; if the first calculation is wrong, we make a second better: we find comfort somewhere.'

*Mrs Grant, Mansfield Park*

*Had not Elinor, in the sad countenance of her sister, seen a check to all mirth, she could have been entertained by Mrs Jennings's endeavours to cure a disappointment in love, by a variety of sweetmeats and olives, and a good fire.*

*Sense and Sensibility*

*Personal size and mental sorrow have certainly no necessary proportions. A large bulky figure has as good a right to be in deep affliction, as the most graceful set of limbs in the world. But, fair or not fair, there are unbecoming conjunctions, which reason will patronize in vain – which taste cannot tolerate – which ridicule will seize.*

*Persuasion*

---

*Marianne had promised to be guided by her mother's opinion, and she submitted to it therefore without opposition, though it proved perfectly different from what she wished and expected, though she felt it to be entirely wrong, formed on mistaken grounds, and that by requiring her longer continuance in London it deprived her of the only possible alleviation of her wretchedness, the personal sympathy of her mother, and doomed her to such society and such scenes as must prevent her ever knowing a moment's rest.*

*Sense and Sensibility*

*She could not help being vexed at the non-appearance of Mr Thorpe, for she not only longed to be dancing, but was likewise aware that, as the real dignity of her situation could not be known, she was sharing with the scores of other young ladies still sitting down all the discredit of wanting a partner.*

Northanger Abbey, of Catherine Morland

' – if I had been treated in that forbidding sort of way, I should have gave it all up in despair. I could not have stood it.'

Lucy Steele, Sense and Sensibility

*They encouraged each other now in the violence of their affliction. The agony of grief which overpowered them at first, was voluntarily renewed, was sought for, was created again and again. They gave themselves up wholly to their sorrow, seeking increase of wretchedness in every reflection that could afford it, and resolved against ever admitting consolation in future.*

*Sense and Sensibility, on Marianne and Mrs Dashwood*

<hr />

'There are few people whom I really love, and still fewer of whom I think well. The more I see of the world, the more am I dissatisfied with it; and every day confirms my belief of the inconsistency of all human characters, and of the little dependence that can be placed on the appearance of merit or sense.'

*Elizabeth Bennet, Pride and Prejudice*

# Misplaced Love

'You could not have made the offer of your hand in any possible way that would have tempted me to accept it.'

*Elizabeth Bennet, Pride and Prejudice*

———————∞○○○∞———————

'It is always incomprehensible to a man that a woman should ever refuse an offer of marriage. A man always imagines a woman to be ready for anybody who asks her.'

*Emma Woodhouse, Emma*

Friendship is certainly the finest balm for the pangs of disappointed love.

*Northanger Abbey*

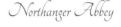

'It is not that I did not think of it, or desire it, but I was proud, too proud to ask again. I did not understand you. Six years of separation and suffering might have been spared.'

*Captain Frederick Wentworth, Persuasion*

*There was a great deal of friendly and of compassionate attachment on his side – but no love.*

*Emma, of Mr Knightley*

━━━━━━━━━━○○○○○○━━━━━━━━━━

*I thought you really very much in love. But you certainly are not at all – there is no concealing it. He is just what he ever was, only more evidently and uniformly devoted to you.*

*Letter to Fanny Knight*

'In such cases as this, it is, I believe, the established mode to express a sense of obligation for the sentiments avowed, however unequally they may be returned. It is natural that obligation should be felt, and if I could feel gratitude, I would now thank you. But I cannot – I have never desired your good opinion, and you have certainly bestowed it most unwillingly.'

Elizabeth Bennet, Pride and Prejudice

*They had no conversation together, no intercourse but what the commonest civility required. Once so much to each other! Now nothing! There had been a time, when of all the large party now filling the drawing-room at Uppercross, they would have found it most difficult to cease to speak to one another... There could have been no two hearts so open, no tastes so similar, no feelings so in unison, no countenances so beloved. Now they were as strangers; nay, worse than strangers, for they could never become acquainted. It was a perpetual estrangement.*

*Persuasion, of Captain Frederick Wentworth and Anne Elliot*

---

*'And so ended his affection. I wonder who first discovered the efficacy of poetry in driving away love!'*

*Elizabeth Bennet, Pride and Prejudice*

'In *marrying* a man
*indifferent* to me, *all risk*
would have been *incurred,*
and *all duty* violated.'

*Anne Elliot, Persuasion*

*How could she have excited serious attachment in a man who had seen so many, and been admired by so many, and flirted with so many, infinitely her superiors; who seemed so little open to serious impressions?*

*Mansfield Park, of Fanny Price's feelings towards Mr Henry Crawford*

—————————∞◦○◦∞—————————

*The conclusion of every imaginary declaration on his side was that she refused him. Their affection was always to subside into friendship. Everything tender and charming was to mark their parting; but still they were to part. When she became sensible of this, it struck her that she could not be very much in love.*

*Emma, of Emma Woodhouse's feelings towards Mr Frank Churchill*

# Marriage

*It is a truth universally acknowledged, that a single man in possession of a good fortune must be in want of a wife.*

*Pride and Prejudice*

---

*'There is nothing she would not do to get married. She would as good as tell you so herself. Do not trust her with any secrets of your own, take warning by me, do not trust her; she has her good qualities, but she has no faith, no honour, no scruples, if she can promote her own advantage.'*

*Miss Watson on Penelope Watson, The Watsons*

*It was, moreover, such a promising thing for her younger daughters, as Jane's marrying so greatly must throw them in the way of other rich men.*

*Pride and Prejudice,* of *Mrs Bennet*

———————————✳———————————

'I could do very well without you, if you were married to a man of such good estate. You must be aware that it is every young woman's duty to accept such a very unexceptionable offer as this.'

*Lady Bertram, Mansfield Park*

'Happiness in marriage is entirely a matter of chance.'

Charlotte Lucas, *Pride and Prejudice*

Elinor sat down to the card table with the melancholy persuasion that Edward was not only without affection for the person who was to be his wife; but that he had not even the chance of being tolerably happy in marriage...

*Sense and Sensibility*

'A woman is not to marry a man
merely because she is asked, or
because he is attached to her,
and can write a tolerable letter.'

Emma Woodhouse, Emma

'I have not a doubt of your doing very well together. Your tempers are by no means unlike. You are each of you so complying, that nothing will ever be resolved on; so easy, that every servant will cheat you; and so generous, that you will always exceed your income.'

Mr Bennet on Jane Bennet and
Mr Bingley's engagement, *Pride and Prejudice*

---

Nothing can be compared to the misery of being bound without love – bound to one, and preferring another; that is a punishment which you do not deserve.

Letter to Fanny Knight

---

'And such is your definition of matrimony and dancing. You will allow, that in both, man has the advantage of choice, woman only the power of refusal; that in both, it is an engagement between man and woman, formed for the advantage of each.'

John Thorpe, *Northanger Abbey*

'To marry *for money*
*I think the wickedest*
*thing in existence.*'

Catherine Morland, Northanger Abbey

If you're interested in finding
out more about our gift books,
follow us on *Twitter:* @Summersdale

www.summersdale.com

'I pay very little regard to what any young person says on the subject of marriage. If they profess a disinclination for it, I only set it down that they have not yet seen the right person.'

*Mrs Grant, Mansfield Park*

———◦◦◦◦◦◦———

And yet I do wish you to marry very much, because I know you will never be happy till you are.

*Letter to Fanny Knight*